JOSEPH AND THE AMAZING TECHNICOLOR DREAMCOAT

Text by Steve Turner
Photography by Michael Le Poer Trench

Marshall Pickering
An Imprint of HarperCollins*Publishers*

Marshall Pickering is an Imprint of
HarperCollins*Religious*
Part of HarperCollins*Publishers*
77-85 Fulham Palace Road, London W6 8JB

First published in Great Britain
in 1993 by Marshall Pickering

1   3   5   7   9   10   8   6   4   2

A catalogue record for this book is
available from the British Library

0 551 02792-4

Printed and bound in Great Britain by
Butler and Tanner Ltd, Frome, Somerset

CONTENTS

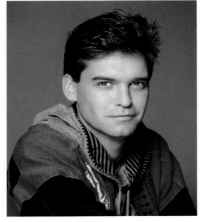

A couple of years ago I had a conversation with a producer at the BBC that made a liar out of me! That conversation went along the lines of, "Have you ever thought of working in the theatre? I'm sure you'd really enjoy the atmosphere". My reply was an emphatic "No, that's one area I'm not remotely interested in, I wouldn't like the repetition and I'm not really a theatrical sort of person!" I still can't believe I said that, but then again I still can't believe anyone ever asked me.

I had been to the opening night of "Joseph" and had really enjoyed myself. When I 'phoned Jason the next day, it was to congratulate him on his performance and to wish him well in the run. After that day I went to watch the show on a number of occasions, and I promise that at no stage did I ever think I'd like to have a go myself, it never entered my mind for a second — not even a brief momentary envy and on that you have my word.

Picture the scene in my house when I received "the phone call" asking if I'd like to consider trying out for the role when Jason went on holiday for six weeks! I very nearly dropped dead with shock. At first I was convinced that there was a terrible mistake, or that this was some misguided prank, after all everyone from Terry Waite to Charlie Brown seemed to have been tipped to take over. How on earth had they come up with my name? After careful questioning my supremely efficient and totally dumb struck management company ascertained that the call was indeed genuine and asked, "Can you sing?" This turned out to be something of a catch-phrase over the next few days. "Wow Phil, that's an amazing opportunity, can you sing?" was all I seemed to hear and the extraordinary thing was, even I didn't have the faintest clue if there was anything with promise lurking in my throat!

It's a great reflection on Sir Andrew Lloyd Webber's talent that he spotted any potential at all from my audition, I was so petrified I'm still not sure which words I sang to "Any dream will do". I can be certain though that my version would not have got to number 1 in the charts. After a polite round of applause I set about the dismembering of "Close every door", convinced by that stage that any door that might have been even slightly ajar had indeed been swiftly closed! Here though is proof of the heat-seeking prescience that Sir Andrew has, I don't know what he saw in the gibbering wreck that stood on that stage but whatever it was, he believed it could cut the mustard.

From that audition to the moment I write these words, my life hasn't been the same. Six weeks of rehearsal followed by six weeks of performances and then to my amazement the offer to continue with the role after Jason left.

If the initial six weeks and 42 performances served to prove anything, it was that any misgivings I had were totally unfounded. After my six week run I could easily have bowed out without losing face but when the opportunity to take over was presented to me I didn't need a moment to decide. I'd had the time of my life, met a group of new friends and realised that every performance and every audience is different, so there's no such thing as repetition.

I can honestly say that I've never had such a fun, rewarding time. I'm loving the experience, the people, the atmosphere and the fact that my first theatrical role just happens to be on the stage of the world's most famous and prestigious theatre. And I'm delighted that this splendid book captures the tremendous excitement and energy of the stage show.

Joseph was a dreamer, his dreams altered the lives of tens of thousands. My dreams haven't had quite such a dramatic effect, however I think I'm proof that in the words of the prologue, "If you think it, want it, dream it, then it's real, you are what you feel".

Never stop dreaming, you never know what might happen!

5th November 1992

CHAPTER I

An Amazing Family

There really was a boy called Joseph. He grew up in Canaan over three and a half thousand years ago with his eleven brothers and their elderly father Jacob.

These were days when you could tell a family's wealth by the number of animals they owned and Jacob was well off in the animal department.

He not only had some fine looking camels and donkeys but huge flocks of sheep and goats which he'd built up through shrewd deals over the years. Then he'd brought his children into the family business.

Although there were twelve boys they shared four different mothers because Jacob had what you might call an 'interesting' background.

'An hour or two
to tell the tale'

The girl of his dreams had been his cousin Rachel and he was all set to marry her after having worked seven years on his uncle's farm as payment when his uncle played a terrible trick on him. On the night of their wedding he swapped her for his other daughter Leah and Jacob didn't know because, as was the custom, she had a veil over her face as they rode off into the sunset after a marvellous feast.

He knew by the next morning though, and his uncle promised that he could also marry Rachel if he worked another seven years. So, Jacob started all over again.

His first four children were with Leah – Reuben, Simeon, Levi and Judah. By this time Rachel was pretty upset that she wasn't producing so she offered Jacob her servant girl, Bilhah, who promptly gave him another two children – Dan and Naphtali.

Now it was Leah's turn to get upset so she shared her servant girl, Zilpah, with Jacob and along came Gad and Asher. Not satisfied with this, Leah herself produced another two sons, Issachar and Zebulun, then a daughter called Dinah (who didn't seem to get mentioned much again in the story).

Rachel by this time was getting pretty anxious. Everyone was having babies but her. She prayed hard about it and then God answered and she gave birth to Joseph. Unfortunately she died giving birth to her next child, who was named Benjamin.

So, as you can see, they were a slightly unusual family and as Rachel had been Jacob's favourite wife, her first son Joseph, became his favourite son. He spoiled him like mad, much to the distress of all the other brothers.

They were also a special family, at least that's what Jacob had always told them. He said that his grandfather Abraham had been informed that they were going to be a huge nation one day. Abraham had said it was God that had made him the promise, so there couldn't be a lot of discussion about that.

Joseph loved these stories that Jacob told about their special family – tales of dreams and angels, of smoking pots and burning torches, of cheating sons and wicked uncles, of wanderings through the desert and journeys to the distant land of Egypt.

The message was that God was going to do his thing, come what may. Sometimes it looked as though things were going to go the other way, as though the whole family was going to be finished right there and then, but God would step in at the last minute as if to say; "You thought I'd forgotten my promise didn't you? Well, I haven't." Come what may, God stayed faithful.

What Joseph didn't know as he listened to these wonderful stories was that one day soon he would be a part of the greatest adventure of them all. He would be taken from the bottom of a pit to the palace of a king and his name would become known around the world for centuries ahead. One day they would even make a musical about him and his multi-coloured coat.

DREAM-BOY

It's hard to tell from what we read whether Joseph was a very wise and diligent teenager when he lived at home or whether he was a pain in the bum. Whichever way, he was not at all popular with his brothers who saw him as a self-centred, stuck-up goody-goody.

When Joseph went off to the fields to check out whether his brothers were working hard and then came back and told his father all the details, maybe he was just taking care of business but they all thought he was a tell-tale and a creep. And they told him so.

When he started parading around in his multi-coloured coat which Jacob had personally embroidered for him maybe he was just displaying a natural interest in fashion but to the brothers it looked like showing off, especially as none of them had ever been given such a fine looking piece of clothing.

'A dazzling coat
of many colours'

When he casually told them of his wonderful dreams, maybe he was a juvenile prophet passing on messages from God, but to the brothers it proved that he was such an ego maniac that even in his dreams he was the family's champion son.

You didn't have to be Sigmund Freud to interpret Joseph's dreams which is just as well, because Sigmund Freud had quite a few centuries to go before he was born.

The first dream, the less extreme one, had all of the boys out harvesting and bundling the corn into sheaves when suddenly, Joseph's sheaf stood upright while his brothers' sheaves bowed down. Did this indicate a superiority complex, or what?

The second dream, the one that even Jacob found a bit much to stomach, featured Joseph again in the lead role being bowed down to by eleven stars plus the sun and moon. Who did he think he was?

Jacob had a go at him about this one but, at the same time, he mulled it over because he'd had a few dreams in his time which had seemed outrageous.

He'd once dreamed of a staircase going up to heaven which had angels walking up and down. At the top of the staircase was God and he had told Jacob that the land of Canaan would one day belong to his descendants.

That dream had changed his life. So he knew you had to be careful when you started dealing with people's dreams.

CHAPTER 2

How to get rid of a pain in the neck

By the end of the last dream the brothers (except for Benjamin who was too small to understand) were white-knuckled with anger. "I could kill that Joe," they all said. The thing was, they meant it too.

One day Jacob sent Joseph off on another fact-finding mission. He was to travel two days north to Shechem and report back on the goings on of the none-too-dedicated brothers who seemed to treat sheep grazing as a lark; as a way of getting away from Jacob and having a little laugh.

Ever eager to please, seventeen year old Joseph set off for Shechem only to find they'd moved on. Fortunately, a local man saw him walking around looking lost and told him that the ten brothers had wandered even further north to Dothan.

It was when the brothers found their peace interrupted by Joseph's arrival that they quickly made their plan to get rid of him. There were two large wells in Dothan (Dothan meant 'two wells') both of which were dry in the summer.

They thought their problems could be solved if Joseph could be termin-ated and then popped into one of these huge holes in the ground. Not much hope of finding a body down there and they could explain to Jacob that he'd been eaten by a wild animal.

PLAN B

But Reuben, the biggest brother of them all, tried to modify the plan. He suggested it would be best if they allowed themselves to be guilty of kidnap and assault but not of murder. Why not toss him into the well alive and leave him? At least the suffering would go on longer. (Actually, although he tried to appeal to their sense of hatred, his real plan was to creep back at night and set Joseph free. He wasn't madly fond of Joseph

but he wanted absolutely no part in his brothers' evil.)

His nine brothers thought this was sound advice and so they grabbed hold of Joseph, ripped his beautiful coloured coat off and hurled him down into the well.

They felt so good after that little exercise that they sat down for a slap-up lunch and as they were eating they noticed a caravan of camels which had travelled down from Gilead and was obviously on its way to Egypt carrying valuable spices.

Judah thought it would be an even better idea to sell Joseph to these Arab merchants. That way they wouldn't have his death on their conscience and they'd get paid too. His brothers agreed so they hauled the screaming boy out of the well and sold him to the passing merchants.

'Poor, poor Joseph'

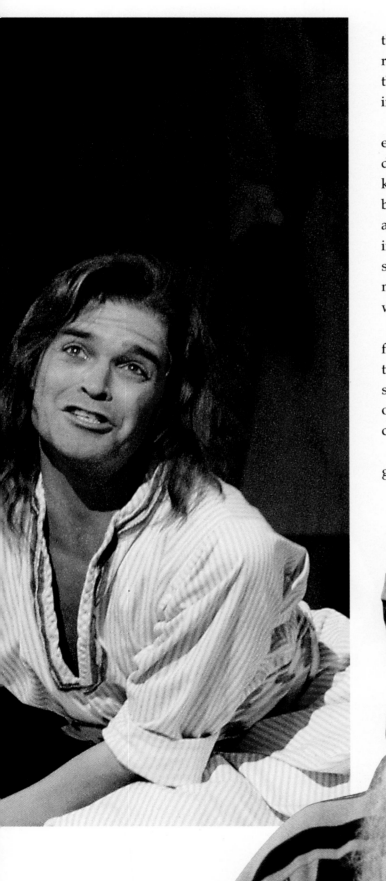

Reuben had left by the time that this happened and when he secretly returned to set Joseph free he found the well empty and had broken down in tears of anguish.

In order to give Jacob a satisfactory explanation for Joseph's sudden disappearance the other brothers had killed a goat, splashed a bit of the blood over the multi-coloured coat and handed it over to Jacob, with tears in their eyes of course, saying that, sadly, Joseph appeared to be no more, that he'd had a fight with a wolf and come second.

The old man was distraught. His favourite son, the only one he could trust, was dead. To show his deep sadness he dressed in clothes made of sacking and wouldn't let anyone comfort him.

It seemed as though God had forgotten him and his family.

CHAPTER 3

A
Mystery
Trip

Joseph was feeling forgotten as well. He couldn't decide whether it was better to be at the bottom of a dry well in Dothan with some hopes of scaling up the sides or stuck with a bunch of foreign merchants who spoke a language he couldn't understand on a six day journey to – where?

He felt hurt and frightened and lost. He'd always tried to do the right thing and now look where it had got him.

At night, when they put up their tents, he would look up at the sky and remember the promise that Jacob had told them God had given, that their family would one day be as numerous as the stars. He really believed that God had a plan but it seemed a very odd way of going about it.

And what about the dreams? After all, he hadn't had one about a sheaf being chucked down a well by ten other sheaves or of being a star that suddenly fell out of the sky. What was going on?

His destination, he eventually learned, was Egypt. Never before had he seen such a busy bustling city. But he wasn't there as a tourist. The merchants took him straight to the slave market to see what they could get for an attractive teenage Hebrew.

ENTER MR POTIPHAR

His buyer was a man named Mr Potiphar, an important Egyptian who lived in a nice house and was in charge of all of Pharaoh's bodyguards. Pharaoh was the Egyptian king and he lived in a palace and was the most important person in the world of those days.

If Joseph had been a prisoner of war, he would have been sent to work in the fields but he was a cash purchase and therefore considered suitable to have around the house and Mr Potiphar had bought well.

For the next ten years or so Joseph worked in Mr Potiphar's home, eventually being put in charge of everything there. At first he couldn't understand Egyptian and had to speak through an interpreter but he then learned the language.

Mr Potiphar didn't believe in this God that Joseph started telling him about because he had been brought up to worship the sun, the source of all light and energy. But there was one thing he couldn't deny; Joseph seemed to have brought a blessing on his house and he wondered whether it was to do with God.

Mr Potiphar was out of the house all day – looking after Pharaoh, throwing people into prison and organising executions. This meant that Joseph got to know Mrs Potiphar quite well.

MRS POTIPHAR
TAKES A FANCY

Now Mrs Potiphar found Joseph quite attractive and exotic. He came from this strange place called Canaan and he was so decent and well behaved. She thought he might appreciate a little fun in between cleaning the dishes and organising the servants but Joseph didn't seem interested.

He said it was something to do with his religion but also that he didn't feel it was fair on Mr Potiphar who had trusted him with everything in the house. It just wasn't right to do things behind his back. He tried to keep out of her way.

Mrs Potiphar didn't give up. She thought that maybe one day he'd show a little weakness and come with her into her wonderful bedroom. But Joseph was strong in what he believed and he wouldn't give in.

One day, when the other servants weren't around, she tried to drag him into her room but he slipped away, leaving his shirt in her hands. Mrs Potiphar felt scorned. She screamed her head off and the servants came running in.

"What is it?" they cried, "What's happened?"

"It's Joseph. He's just tried to attack me while Mr Potiphar is out but I fought him off and he ran away leaving his shirt behind!"

Mr Potiphar was none too pleased when he heard this story. This was taking household duties much too far. He'd trusted Joseph completely and this was how he was rewarded.

There was no alternative, Joseph would have to be put into prison and so in he went, not with the common criminals, but with those who'd done wrong to Pharoah and his officials.

'Potiphar had very
few cares'

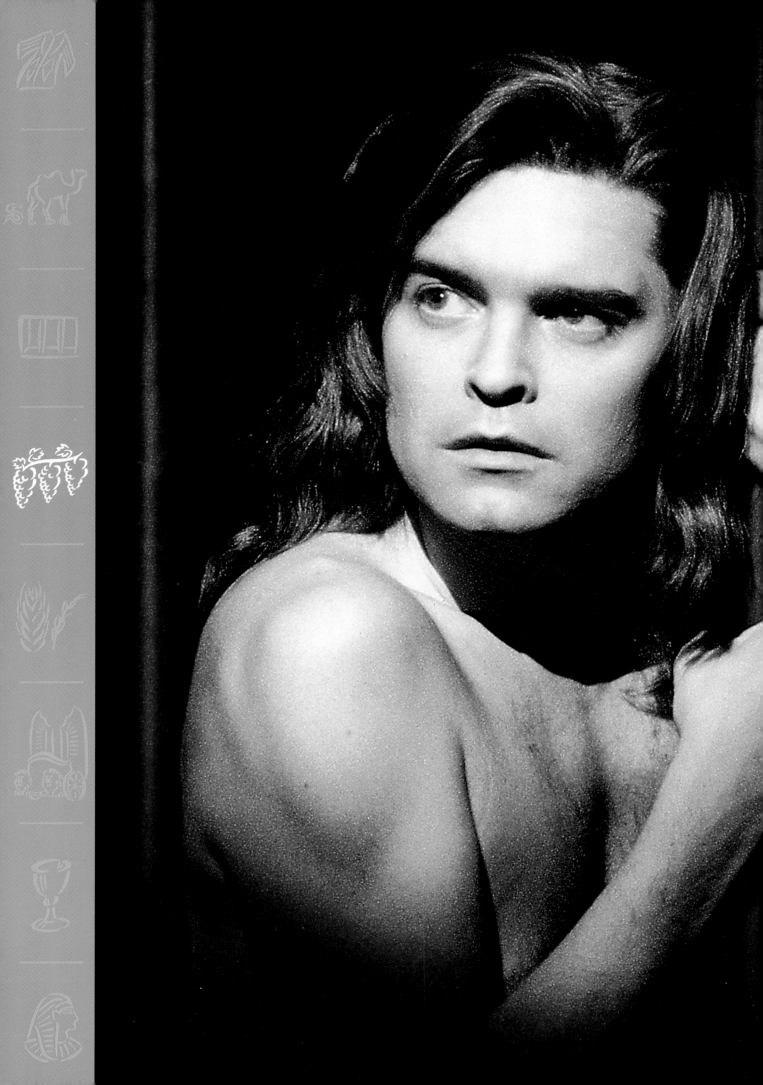

CHAPTER 4

Cell Mates

If there was one lesson Joseph had learned since leaving home it was how to make the best of a bad situation. In prison it would be no different. He would survive.

Cheerfully he went around the prison being nice to people, talking about how wonderful God was and asking if there were any more jobs he could do. The Chief Guard was rather partial to a prisoner like Joseph who seemed to appreciate a life behind bars. He soon found some responsibilities for him – like looking after some of the other prisoners when he wasn't around.

It wasn't long after Joseph took up residence that Pharaoh's butler and baker came and joined him.

Apparently they'd been caught up in a major tiff, the details of which weren't clear, and they'd been banished to the dungeon until their case could be looked at.

They were both in charge of food departments in the palace. The butler looked after the vineyards and made sure that Pharaoh drank only the best wine. The baker was responsible for preparing all the food.

One night both of these men had food dreams and they were upset that the usual magicians and soothsayers weren't around to give them an interpretation. Joseph, realising that the dreams were from God, offered to help out.

FIRST THE GOOD NEWS

The butler's dream was a wine dream. He said he had seen a vine with three branches which produced clusters of ripe grapes. He then saw himself picking the grapes and squeezing them into Pharaoh's cup just as he had done in the days before he lost his job.

"The three branches equal three days," said Joseph. "The meaning of your dream is that in three days Pharaoh will ask to see you and you'll be acquitted of the crime he thinks you've committed and you'll be back at work."

The butler liked this interpretation. It was just the sort of thing he wanted to hear. "Glad you liked it," said Joseph. "By the way, when you get out could you ask Pharaoh to spare me a thought?"

BAD LUCK, BAKER

Impressed with the good news that the butler had heard, the baker began to tell his dream. This time it was about three bread baskets piled up high on his head and some birds that swooped down and started pecking at the basket.

Joseph had to bite his lip over this one. "Ahem. The three baskets represent three days," said Joseph.

"In three days Pharaoh will request to see you . . . and then you'll be hanged. The birds you saw are the birds that will eat your body as it swings from the rope." The baker didn't say anything more. He'd heard enough.

The third day was Pharaoh's birthday and he wanted to do something special for his party so he threw a grand banquet at his palace for all his close friends and officials and, just as things really started to swing, he called for the butler and the baker.

As the music stopped and the crowd hushed he asked the butler to step forward. "Butler," said Pharaoh, "I find you innocent of the charges brought against you. Tomorrow you will start again in your old job." The party goers applauded.

"Baker," said Pharaoh, "I find you guilty of the charges brought against you. Tonight you will be hanged by the neck until dead."

The silence continued as the guards escorted the baker away. But in his moment of relief the butler completely forgot to mention Joseph's plight to Pharaoh and so Joseph continued to sit alone in his cell, pondering what all of this meant. He had never felt so lonely in his life. His family had probably forgotten him, the butler certainly had, perhaps God had too. So much for his dreams.

'Close every door'

CHAPTER 5

Pharaoh's Nightlife

It was two years later that Pharoah found himself waking up in a cold sweat after a pair of scary dreams.

In the first one he saw himself standing in the reedy land beside the river Nile minding his own business when out of the water stepped seven jumbo sized cows.

At this point he felt okay because cows were a good sign in his culture. They were a symbol of fertility. But then, right behind the fat cows, came seven scrawny cows who proceeded to chew up and swallow their more portly relatives, but without putting on any weight themselves.

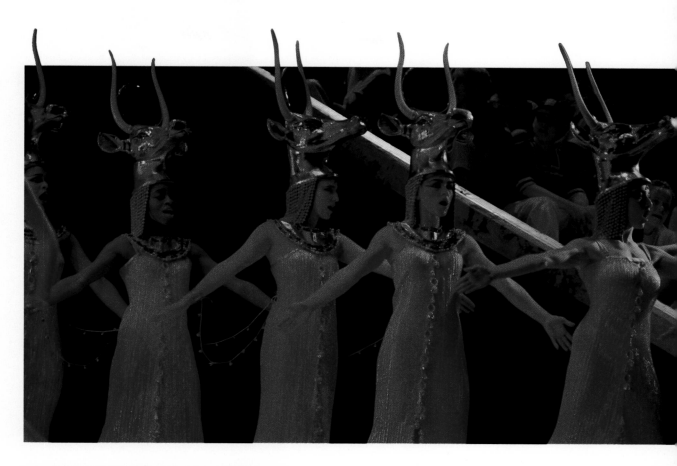

In the second dream he saw a stalk of wheat with seven ears of grain on it. Again this looked like a good omen, because Egypt was the grain capital of the world. But then seven withered ears of grain which had been ravaged by bad weather sprung up and they proceeded to swallow the healthy grains.

He was troubled about the meaning of these dreams and none of the people he paid to interpret his dreams and help him plan for the future had a clue what they meant.

The butler, who overheard all this, suddenly remembered the Hebrew prisoner who had done such a good job for him.

"There is a man I think might be able to help you," he said. "That time I was thrown in prison with the baker there was a man in there, a young Hebrew, and he told us the meaning of our dreams and, in both cases, what he said would happen came true. It was amazing!"

FETCH THE PRISONER!

So Pharaoh immediately sent for Joseph who was so dirty and stubbly that he had to be bathed and shaved and put into nice clothes before he was fit to stand before the most important and powerful king in the world.

"I hear that you can understand dreams," said Pharaoh after Joseph had entered the room and sat down, "and you're able to tell exactly what they mean."

"It's not me that does it," said Joseph. "I don't have any special ability but sometimes God gives someone a dream and then he tells me what the meaning is."

Pharaoh found Joseph's humility refreshing. A lot of people in his position would be bragging about their talents or trying to strike a deal.

He told him the two dreams and waited to see what Joseph would say.

PHARAOH'S DREAMS EXPLAINED

Joseph pondered a moment and then said; "The seven fat cows and the seven good ears of corn both mean the same thing. They are seven years of great harvests that you are going to experience in Egypt.

"But the seven thin cows and the seven straggly ears

'Seven fat cows came up out of the Nile, uh-huh'

of corn mean the same thing too. They are the seven years of famine that will follow on. These years are going to be so bad that no-one will remember the good years.

"The reason God has given the dream is to offer a warning so that you have time to plan ahead."

At this point Joseph became animated and excited. What God was showing him was not just the problem but the means of solving it.

"What you need to do is this. You need to find an administrator for the country, someone good at analysing problems and also someone whom the people will trust. That man needs to appoint commissioners for each area of the country to make sure that during the seven good years, a fifth of everything produced is kept in storage.

"In that way you'll have a surplus of food stored in each city which can then be used when the bad years come."

GOVERNOR JOSEPH

Just as Potiphar had once noticed that there was something different about Joseph, that the God he spoke about really seemed to live through him, Pharaoh decided, and his officials agreed, that Joseph was that man.

"You've got yourself a job," said Pharaoh. "You've proved that you are the most wise and discerning

JOSEPH AND THE AMAZING TECHNICOLOR DREAMCOAT

man in Egypt. Everything that you think we should do to protect ourselves from famine, you organise it."

And Pharaoh took the unprecedented step of giving Joseph almost total control of Egypt. He would remain the King but Joseph would be his second in command.

He gave Joseph his signet ring, so he could put the royal seal on any document, dressed him in fine robes and put a chain of office around his neck. He looked like a prince.

A procession was arranged in which Joseph travelled in his own chariot just behind Pharaoh so that all the people would recognise how important he was.

It was only now that Joseph could see that all his hardships had been to prepare him for this. Through the disappointments, the betrayals, the

imprisonment, the loneliness, his God had been training him for this special job.

He was now thirty years old and he married an Egyptian woman, Potiphera, and they had two children – Manasseh and Ephraim. For the first seven years of his swanky new job he buzzed around the country making sure that every region was storing a fifth of its grain in huge barns, ready for the bad years.

Just as the dream had indicated, these were great years of bumper harvests. There was so much grain brought in that Joseph stopped keeping records. Grain mountains piled up everywhere.

CHAPTER 6

Dreams
Come True

At the end of the seventh year the famine bit. It was not just in Egypt, but in all the countries around. The rain didn't come, the severe easterly winds blew, the sun beat down and the ground was parched.

But because of the seven year savings plan there was plenty of food in Egypt and Joseph organised the opening of the storage barns.

News of Egypt's surplus spread to the countries around and soon thousands of foreigners were coming to the country in search of food. Again Joseph organised them. If too many were allowed in it could disrupt the economy. They might try to overthrow Pharaoh. He also had to make sure that no enemy spies were let in.

He made sure that the borders were guarded and that all the foreigners were escorted back out of the country once they had made their purchases.

CUSTOMERS FROM CANAAN — OR SPIES?

Joseph's brothers, whom he now hadn't seen for twenty years, were among the foreign visitors. They had been sent by their father Jacob who was running short of food and could see that his family would soon be wiped out by the famine. He had asked only that they leave young Benjamin behind because, having lost one of Rachel's sons, he could not bear the thought of losing the other. It would break his heart. He still grieved for Joseph.

It happened that when the ten brothers arrived in Egypt they had to be scrutinised by Joseph the governor. As they approached him he recognised them immediately and he was nearly overcome with emotion but none of them knew that this foreign ruler standing in front of them was the teenage boy they tossed in a pit hoping for his death, twenty years before.

They walked up to him and each bowed low before him, as was the custom, and in that moment Joseph realised that his dreams had come true. His boyhood dream was coming true before his eyes.

Through an interpreter Joseph began to quiz them, enjoying playing a little game with them to see how sorry they were for what they'd done. This was his moment of triumph. It was almost like being a guest at his own funeral, listening to what the mourners said about him.

"Where are you from?" he asked.

"We're from Canaan," they said. "We're here to buy food."

"You're from Canaan alright," said Joseph, "But you're not here for the food. I believe you're here to check out our defences and make plans of our streets. You're spies!"

They couldn't believe they were being accused of spying. The

thought was furthest from their minds. They were terrified that they'd got themselves into big trouble; that they'd been tricked into staying behind as slaves.

"We're all from the same family," they assured him. "Our father had twelve boys. He has stayed behind with the youngest and one brother died some time ago."

"Just as I said," said Joseph. "You're spies! I'll test your story. Nine of you stay here in Egypt, in prison, while one of you goes back to Canaan and brings back this brother of yours. If you're telling the truth, all will be clear If you're not, then you're obviously spies."

He then put them into custody for three days, after which he changed his mind very slightly.

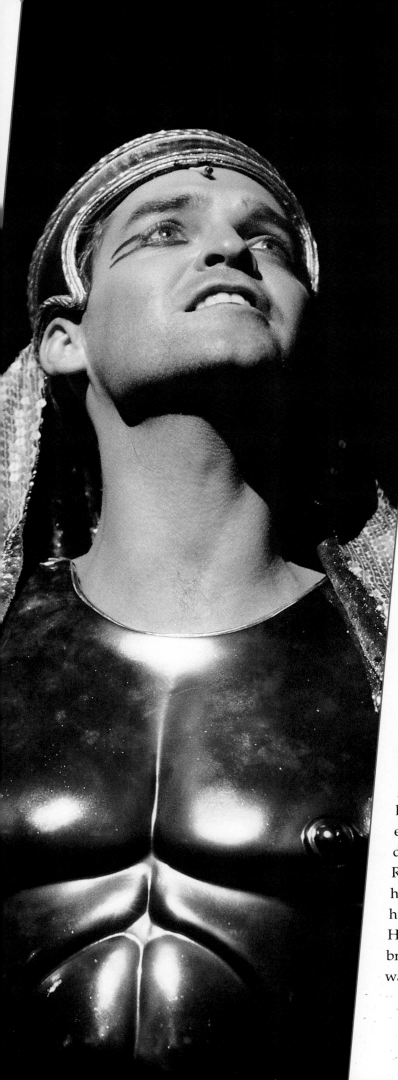

TROUBLE AND MORE TROUBLE

"I tell you what," he said. "There's no need for all of you to stay in prison. Why not take the grain you want back home, leave just one of you behind here and then return and bring your brother."

It sounded a much more reasonable deal but still they were worried. Their father would be devastated if they returned as nine brothers and then had to take Benjamin away from him.

Reuben, the only brother who had argued to save Joseph all those years ago, immediately saw it all as a punishment from God for the way they had acted.

He, of course, had no idea that the Egyptian governor standing before him could understand his language so he said to his brothers. "Didn't I tell you not to do it in the first place? You heard what I said, you saw how distressed he was but you wouldn't listen."

Joseph couldn't hold back the tears hearing his brothers talk of those events from so long along, and to discover for the first time that Reuben had wanted to save him. He had to turn away from them to hide his emotions.

He then asked for Simeon to be the brother that was left behind as he was the second eldest and possibly

'Eleven brothers, good
men and true'

therefore the one responsible for trying to kill him as a teenager.

He asked his servants to pack the grain in each of the brothers' bags, give them food and water for their journey and slip the money they had paid back into their purses. This was to act as a little frightener.

It was when they stopped at an inn on the way back that one of them noticed that his silver had been replaced. He was terrified that the Egyptians would now accuse him of escaping without paying. Matters got worse when they arrived home and they each found that their money had been put back.

CHAPTER 7

Back to Egypt

Their father Jacob got into a real state when the brothers asked him to allow Benjamin to go back to Egypt with them. He now feared the worst was about to happen but both Reuben and Judah pleaded with him, saying they would make themselves personally responsible for his safe return.

The old man insisted that they take enough silver to pay back the money if a mistake had been made and also to pack a gift of spices, nuts and honey to give to the governor.

They hurried back down to Egypt with Benjamin and presented themselves to the governor, whom they still did not recognise. As soon as he saw them coming he told his steward to prepare a great banquet for them at his home.

The news of the banquet completely unnerved the brothers. It was a ploy to capture them, perhaps. They doubted they'd come out of this alive. Whatever was happening they were sure it had something to do with the money that had mysteriously found its way back into their bags.

To clear themselves, they found a steward and explained what had happened, telling him that they had brought extra money to pay him back.

"Don't worry," said the steward, "It was your God who gave you the money back." Then he reunited them with Simeon and gave them all water to wash their feet with and food for their donkeys.

When the governor arrived at midday, they offered him their fine Canaanite gifts and fell down at his feet. He quietly asked them how they were and then quizzed them about their father. "Is he alright?" he asked, "Is he still alive?"

Then he noticed Benjamin, now a grown man, and the only one he wouldn't have recognised. As he looked on his only full-blood brother he became so overwhelmed with emotion that he actually had to leave the room. He cried alone in another room and then washed his face and returned to tell the stewards to start serving food.

What next amazed the brothers and convinced them that something strange was afoot was that they were seated at the table according to their ages; Reuben, the eldest, at the top of the table followed by Simeon, Levi, Judah, Dan, Naphtali, Gad, Asher, Issachar, Zebulun and then, young Benjamin. How could the governor have known their ages?

WHO'S THE THIEF?

When they had finished eating the stewards again filled the men's sacks with grain to take back to Canaan and replaced the money. But this time the governor also told them to conceal one of his silver cups in the top of Benjamin's sack.

They set off at dawn the next day and before they had gone far a steward chased after them and stopped them and asked which of

'One of you has stolen my precious golden cup'

them had stolen the governor's silver cup. They all replied confidently that they were all innocent. It must be a mistake. They said that if the cup should be found on any one of them that one should be executed.

The steward, having noted their positions at the dinner table, searched them from Reuben down to the youngest. When he got to Benjamin's sack, just as the other brothers were breathing a sigh of relief, the silver cup fell from the mouth of his sack.

They were dumbfounded. They began tearing their clothes and weeping. This was their worst dream come true. The shock of this would kill their father for sure.

CHAPTER 8

The Final Test

The brothers got back on to their donkeys and made their way back to Egypt for what looked like the worst day of their lives. They came to the governor's house and stood before him with their heads hung low.

"What can I say?", said Judah. "How can we prove to you that we are innocent? We've done bad things in the past and God has found us out. We'll now have to become your slaves, all of us, including the one whose sack the cup was found in."

But Joseph said, "Don't worry. Only the person in whose sack the cup was found need stay. The rest of you can leave."

Judah begged him not to take Benjamin. He explained how Joseph and Benjamin had been his father's two favourite children and how Joseph had been killed and Jacob's life was now bound up with Benjamin.

He told how their father had begged them not to take Benjamin for fear of something terrible happening and how he and Reuben had faithfully promised to look after him. Judah begged Joseph to let him be the one that stayed behind as a slave and to let Benjamin go home.

"I AM JOSEPH"

At this the governor's eyes welled with tears. He could see that they were no longer the arrogant brothers he'd once known but men who cared for their father and their brother and who were sorry for all they'd done wrong. He asked all his stewards and

'A chariot of gold'

servants to go out, leaving him and his brothers alone in the room.

He turned to his brothers and said, "I am Joseph, the brother you tried to kill." Then he broke down crying and wept so loudly that everyone in the house could hear him.

"Is my father still alive?", he asked, but his brothers were stunned into silence. They were terrified. Was this a trick? Was it a ghost? Was it a further punishment from God?

"Don't be afraid," he said, "I'm not angry with you. It was all part of God's plan because there are going to be another five years of famine and I was sent ahead to make preparations for you. We are the chosen family and if this hadn't happened we would all have been wiped out.

"What I want now is for you to go back to Canaan and to bring back Jacob and all your families and animals because if you stay where

you are you'll be devastated by the famine. I want you to come and live in Goshen, to be near me and to graze your animals."

Then he threw his arms around each of the brothers and wept with them all for sheer joy.

The brothers sped back to Canaan and tried to explain to Jacob that his son Joseph was now governor of Egypt. He couldn't take it in until he saw all the royal carts that had been sent up to collect their belongings and then he believed their story. The best thing of all for him was to know that he'd see Joseph again before he died. What a miracle!

So a convoy of over eighty people with donkeys, camels, sheep and goats made its way down to Egypt. When he saw them approaching, Joseph rode out in a chariot to meet his family and when he at last saw his father he ran to embrace him. It was the most over-whelming reunion; neither father nor son could bear to let each other go. The rest of the family wondered whether they should start unpacking; it looked as though they were going to be there all day!

'Go, go, go Joseph'

POSTSCRIPT

Jacob lived with his family in Egypt for another seventeen years and when he died his body was taken back to Canaan to be buried alongside his father Isaac and his grandfather Abraham.

His children became known as the Israelites and after many years in Egypt they did actually come back to the land of Canaan, just as Jacob had been promised, and one of their great, great, great, great grand-children was Jesus of Nazareth, whose life and death would bless the whole world.